Self-Care
PLANNER

This planner belongs to:

Created by
Sheleen Lepar and Helene Pam
Purple Splash Studios

Self-care is an act of self-love.

The Journey Begins Here

Congratulations for starting this important self-care journey!
You deserve this! Self-care is not a luxury, it is a necessity.

Before you dig in, here's a quick overview.

A lot of thought, research, and love went into creating this planner and we hope that you will get much value and enjoyment from the exercises, techniques, and trackers.

The goal is to empower you to:

- Create an intentional plan to care for your physical, emotional, social, and spiritual health.
- Achieve, track, and celebrate the completion of your goals.
- Explore new routines and form positive habits.
- Reduce anxiety, and improve your mood and self-esteem.

Here are some activities that you will find in this planner:

- MY SELF-CARE PLAN: Put together a plan on how to better take care of yourself. (p.6)
- MY PERFECT DAY: Visualize your ideal day and identify changes that you can make. (p.8)
- MY 'PICK ME UP' PLAN: Make a plan to use when you are feeling down. (p.11)
- MY SUPPORT TEAM: Identify the people that you can turn to when you need support. (p.12)
- MY AFFIRMATIONS: Create positive statements to help adjust your perspective. (p.15)
- GOAL ACTION PLAN: Put together a plan to set you up to achieve specific goals. (p.17)
- SELF-CARE CHECKLISTS: Instill healthy habits with monthly checklists. (p.28)
- 30 DAY TRACKERS/CHALLENGES: Explore new routines, keep motivated, and solidify positive habits with these fun trackers. There are templates to track your emotions, sleep, water drinking, gratitude, exercise, reading, acts of kindness, and blank templates to create your own. It even includes Doodle Challenges to encourage creativity and help bring you into the present moment. (p.35)
- 9 COLORFUL QUOTE PAGES: Find inspiration throughout the process.

Feel free to work on the pages that are meaningful to you and to reach out if you have questions or thoughts. For additional templates, you can find self-care planner printables on our website.

Let's do this!
Sheleen and Helene, (the mom-daughter team)
www.PurpleSplashStudios.com

Self-care is...

S peaking kindly to yourself

E xercising your body and mind

L etting yourself laugh and cry

F ocusing on being positive

C onnecting deeply with others

A ppreciating what you have

R esting, relaxing, and restoring

E ating well to nourish yourself

- Helene Pam

Reflection

Think about the past few months and unlock opportunities for growth.

What has been great the last few months?

_____

_____

What is something valuable that I have learned?

_____

_____

In what way can my thinking be more positive?

_____

_____

In what way can I better manage and express my emotions?

_____

_____

In what way can I better nourish and energize my body?

_____

_____

In what way can I better nourish and energize my soul?

_____

Example Self-Care Plan

Here are examples of ways that you can better take care of yourself and improve things in the various areas of your life.

Health/Growth Areas:
BODY= Physical   MIND= Intellectual   HEART= Emotional/Social   SOUL= Spiritual

Get inspired to create your own plan using the examples below.

BODY

Stretch more

8 hours of sleep

Drink more water

Work out 4 times/wk

Eat more fruit & veg

MIND

Read more

Think positively

Learn something new

Watch inspiring videos

Take a class

BALANCE

HEART

Ask for support

More present w/family

More plans w/friends

Acts of kindness

Laugh more

SOUL

Meditate

Listen to music/sing

Give gratitude

Time in nature

Journal

My Self-Care Plan

How can you better take care of yourself and improve things in the various areas of your life?

Health/Growth Areas:
BODY= Physical   MIND= Intellectual   HEART= Emotional/Social   SOUL= Spiritual

Add things you want to improve in each area.

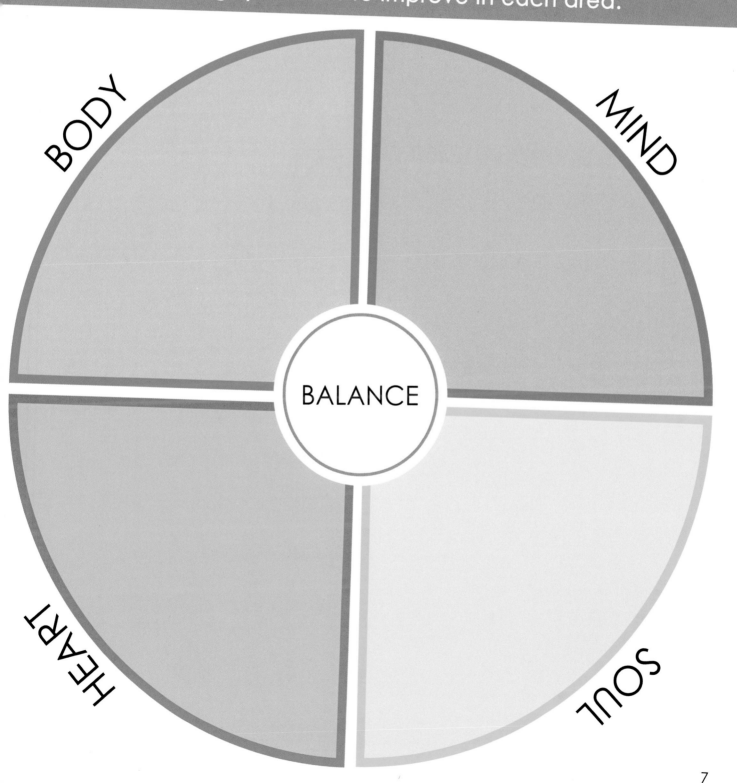

BODY

MIND

BALANCE

HEART

SOUL

My Perfect Day

What would your perfect day look like?

Morning

Afternoon

Night

How to Live My Perfect Day

Morning	
Afternoon	
Night	

Take time to do what makes your **soul** **happy.**

My Support Team

When you need support, it is helpful to have a list of people who you can trust as well as to know how they can help you. These people can be your family, friends, community members, teachers, colleagues, health professionals, or mentors.

Create a summary of your team and how they can help you.

Name: _____

Help by: _____

_____

Name: _____

Help by: _____

_____

Name: _____

Help by: _____

_____

Name: _____

Help by: _____

_____

Name: _____

Help by: _____

_____

Name: _____

Help by: _____

_____

Name: _____

Help by: _____

_____

Name: _____

Help by: _____

_____

Your mind will always ✳ believe ✳ what you tell it.

Feed it hope.

Feed it truth.

Feed it love.

My Affirmations

Repeating positive statements, like "I am enough",
is a self-talk technique that can adjust your attitude and
create positive habits. It is effective at improving your life as it
imprints your intentions and desires on your subconscious mind.

Create affirmations that you can say daily or when you need it.

Tip: Make sure your affirmations are grounded in truth.

6 months from now you can be in a completely different space

mentally,
spiritually,
physically,
or financially.

In what way would you like your life to be different?

My 6 Key Goals

Once you have selected your key goals below, on the following pages you will add details and make a plan for each.

1

2

3

4

5

6

Goal Action Plan

DATE

Pick a goal and create an action plan.

My goal: (be specific)

It's important to me because _____

_____

I'd like to achieve it by (date) _____

Who can help me with this? _____

I will know I've met my goal when _____

What could hold me back from achieving my goal?

_____

I can overcome this by _____

_____

Three steps to make it happen: (add these to your calendar)

Achieved:

1) _____

2) _____

3) _____

18

Goal Action Plan

Pick a goal and create an action plan.

My goal: (be specific)

It's important to me because _____

_____

_____

I'd like to achieve it by (date) _____

Who can help me with this? _____

I will know I've met my goal when _____

_____

What could hold me back from achieving my goal?

_____

I can overcome this by _____

_____

Three steps to make it happen: (add these to your calendar)

1) _____ ☐   Achieved:

2) _____ ☐

3) _____ ☐

Goal Action Plan

Pick a goal and create an action plan.

My goal: (be specific)

It's important to me because _____

_____

_____

I'd like to achieve it by (date) _____

Who can help me with this? _____

I will know I've met my goal when _____

_____

What could hold me back from achieving my goal?

_____

I can overcome this by _____

_____

Three steps to make it happen: (add these to your calendar)

Achieved:

1) _____

2) _____

3) _____

Goal Action Plan

Pick a goal and create an action plan.

My goal: (be specific)

It's important to me because _____

_____

_____

I'd like to achieve it by (date) _____

Who can help me with this? _____

I will know I've met my goal when _____

_____

What could hold me back from achieving my goal?

_____

I can overcome this by _____

Three steps to make it happen: (add these to your calendar)

1) _____   Achieved:

2) _____

3) _____

Goal Action Plan

Pick a goal and create an action plan.

My goal: (be specific)

It's important to me because _____

_____

_____

I'd like to achieve it by (date) _____

Who can help me with this? _____

I will know I've met my goal when _____

_____

What could hold me back from achieving my goal?

_____

I can overcome this by _____

_____

Three steps to make it happen: (add these to your calendar)

Achieved:

1) _____ ☐

2) _____ ☐

3) _____ ☐

22

Goal Action Plan

Pick a goal and create an action plan.

My goal: (be specific)

It's important to me because _____

_____

_____

I'd like to achieve it by (date) _____

Who can help me with this? _____

I will know I've met my goal when _____

_____

What could hold me back from achieving my goal?

_____

I can overcome this by _____

_____

Three steps to make it happen: (add these to your calendar)

1) _____   ☐   Achieved:

2) _____   ☐

3) _____   ☐

23

Goal Task List

This page is helpful for bigger goals with multiple steps.

Pick a goal and break it out into actionable tasks.

My goal: (be specific)

Target date to complete goal:

List the tasks or action items needed to help complete the goal. Assign target dates to each task. Add the dates to your calendar.

TASK/ACTION ITEM	TARGET DATE	✓
		☐
		☐
		☐
		☐
		☐
		☐
		☐
		☐
		☐
		☐

Goal completed on: _____

Time to celebrate!

Goal Task List

This page is helpful for bigger goals with multiple steps.

Pick a goal and break it out into actionable tasks.

My goal: (be specific)

Target date to complete goal:

List the tasks or action items needed to help complete the goal.
Assign target dates to each task. Add the dates to your calendar.

TASK/ACTION ITEM	TARGET DATE	✓
		☐
		☐
		☐
		☐
		☐
		☐
		☐
		☐
		☐
		☐

Goal completed on: _____   *Time to celebrate!*

Goal Task List

This page is helpful for bigger goals with multiple steps.

Pick a goal and break it out into actionable tasks.

My goal: (be specific)

Target date to complete goal:

List the tasks or action items needed to help complete the goal.
Assign target dates to each task. Add the dates to your calendar.

TASK/ACTION ITEM	TARGET DATE	✓
		☐
		☐
		☐
		☐
		☐
		☐
		☐
		☐
		☐
		☐

Goal completed on: _____

Time to celebrate!

26

Goal Task List

This page is helpful for bigger goals with multiple steps.

Pick a goal and break it out into actionable tasks.

My goal: (be specific)

Target date to complete goal:

List the tasks or action items needed to help complete the goal. Assign target dates to each task. Add the dates to your calendar.

TASK/ACTION ITEM	TARGET DATE	✓
		☐
		☐
		☐
		☐
		☐
		☐
		☐
		☐
		☐
		☐

Goal completed on: _____ Time to celebrate!

Get into the habit of
asking yourself,

"Does this support
the life I'm trying
to create?"

NEXT UP

The following 6 pages contain 31 day Self-Care Checklists.
These will help you track your behavior for
6 months and instill healthy habits.

Half of the checklist pages include things to track. The other
half are empty so that you can fill them out as you wish.

If you need additional templates, find our printable pack on
www.PurpleSplashStudios.com.

Self-Care Checklist

Keep track of your self-care to instill healthy habits.

DATES

Hours of sleep								
Glasses of water								
Minutes exercised								
Fruit eaten								
Vegetables eaten								
Time with family								
Acts of kindness								
Music/singing time								
Creative time								
Time in nature								
Laughed								
Tidy/clean up time								
Minutes read								
Gratitude/journal								
Meditated								
Felt positive								

Self-Care Checklist

Keep track of your self-care to instill healthy habits.

Hours of sleep	
Glasses of water	
Minutes exercised	
Fruit eaten	
Vegetables eaten	
Time with family	
Acts of kindness	
Music/singing time	
Creative time	
Time in nature	
Laughed	
Tidy/clean up time	
Minutes read	
Gratitude/journal	
Meditated	
Felt positive	

Self-Care Checklist

Keep track of your self-care to instill healthy habits.

	DATES
Hours of sleep	
Glasses of water	
Minutes exercised	
Fruit eaten	
Vegetables eaten	
Time with family	
Acts of kindness	
Music/singing time	
Creative time	
Time in nature	
Laughed	
Tidy/clean up time	
Minutes read	
Gratitude/journal	
Meditated	
Felt positive	

Self-Care Checklist

Keep track of your self-care to instill healthy habits.

DATES

Self-Care Checklist

Keep track of your self-care to instill healthy habits.

Self-Care Checklist

Keep track of your self-care to instill healthy habits.

DATES

It's not about perfect.
It's about persistence.

when you keep moving forward, despite setbacks, that's when transformation happens.

NEXT UP

The following 20 pages contain various 30 Day Trackers/ "Challenges". These will help you to explore new routines, keep motivated, and solidify positive habits.

There are templates to track your emotions, sleep, water drinking, gratitude, exercise, reading, acts of kindness, and blank templates to create your own. There are even Doodle Challenges to encourage creativity and bring you into the present moment.

Work on the challenges that are meaningful to you. If you need additional templates, find our printable pack on www.PurpleSplashStudios.com.

30 Day Emotions Tracker

Create a key to track your emotions for 30 days.

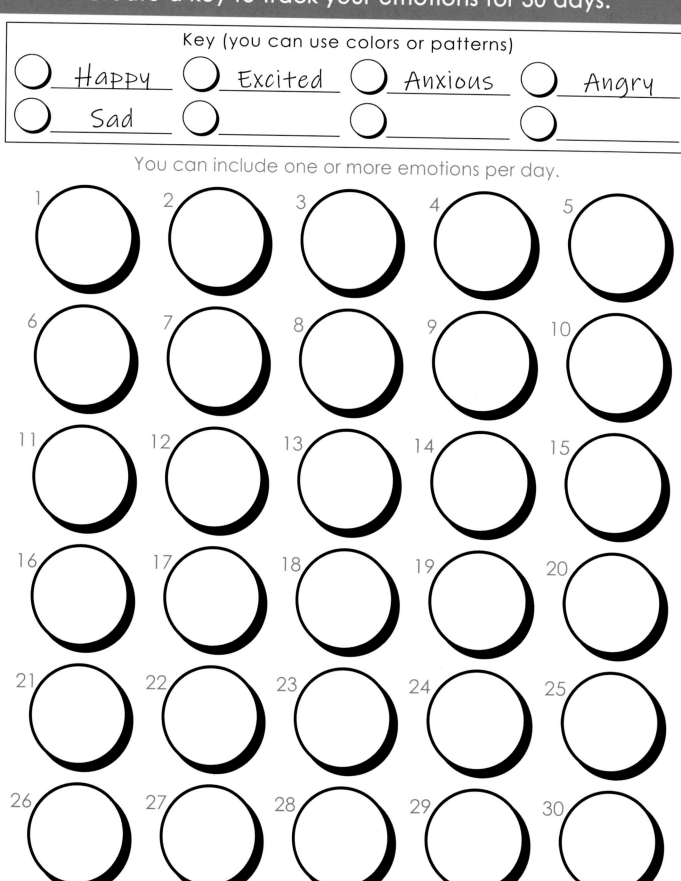

Key (you can use colors or patterns)

○ ___Happy___   ○ ___Excited___   ○ ___Anxious___   ○ ___Angry___

○ ___Sad___   ○ _____   ○ _____   ○ _____

You can include one or more emotions per day.

1   2   3   4   5

6   7   8   9   10

11   12   13   14   15

16   17   18   19   20

21   22   23   24   25

26   27   28   29   30

30 Day Emotions Tracker

Create a key to track your emotions for 30 days.

Key (you can use colors or patterns)

○ Happy ○ Excited ○ Anxious ○ Angry

○ Sad ○ _____ ○ _____ ○ _____

You can include one or more emotions per day.

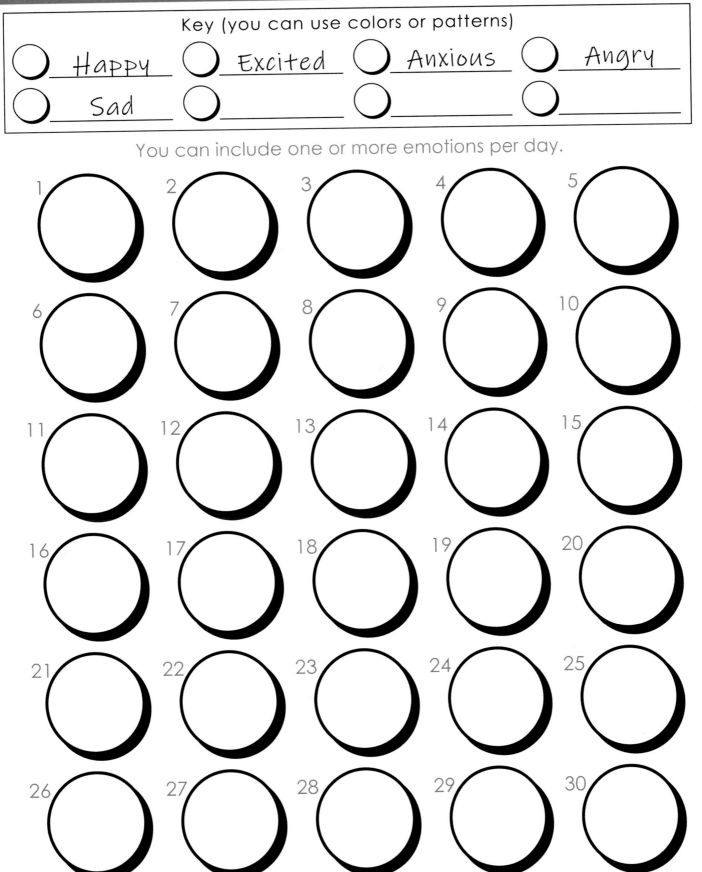

1 2 3 4 5

6 7 8 9 10

11 12 13 14 15

16 17 18 19 20

21 22 23 24 25

26 27 28 29 30

30 Day Sleep Tracker

My Goal: _____   Start Date: _____

Zzz 1	Zzz 2	Zzz 3	Zzz 4	Zzz 5
Zzz 6	Zzz 7	Zzz 8	Zzz 9	Zzz 10
Zzz 11	Zzz 12	Zzz 13	Zzz 14	Zzz 15
Zzz 16	Zzz 17	Zzz 18	Zzz 19	Zzz 20
Zzz 21	Zzz 22	Zzz 23	Zzz 24	Zzz 25
Zzz 26	Zzz 27	Zzz 28	Zzz 29	Zzz 30

Tip: Track your emotions at the same time to see if there is a link between the hours of sleep you are getting and your emotions.

30 Day Sleep Tracker

My Goal: _____ Start Date: _____

Zzz 1	Zzz 2	Zzz 3	Zzz 4	Zzz 5
Zzz 6	Zzz 7	Zzz 8	Zzz 9	Zzz 10
Zzz 11	Zzz 12	Zzz 13	Zzz 14	Zzz 15
Zzz 16	Zzz 17	Zzz 18	Zzz 19	Zzz 20
Zzz 21	Zzz 22	Zzz 23	Zzz 24	Zzz 25
Zzz 26	Zzz 27	Zzz 28	Zzz 29	Zzz 30

Tip: Track your emotions at the same time to see if there is a link between the hours of sleep you are getting and your emotions.

30 Day Water Challenge

My Goal: _____   Start Date: _____

1   2   3   4   5

6   7   8   9   10

11   12   13   14   15

16   17   18   19   20

21   22   23   24   25

26   27   28   29   30

40

30 Day Water Challenge

Track how many glasses or bottles of water you drink for 30 days.

My Goal: _____ Start Date: _____

1

2

3

4

5

6

7

8

9

10

11

12

13

14

15

16

17

18

19

20

21

22

23

24

25

26

27

28

29

30

Color in the flowers and think of the things that you are grateful for.

Happiness
grows from
a garden of
gratitude.

- Helene Pam

30 Days of Gratitude

1. _____
2. _____
3. _____
4. _____
5. _____
6. _____
7. _____
8. _____
9. _____
10. _____
11. _____
12. _____
13. _____
14. _____
15. _____

16. _____
17. _____
18. _____
19. _____
20. _____
21. _____
22. _____
23. _____
24. _____
25. _____
26. _____
27. _____
28. _____
29. _____
30. _____

30 Days of Gratitude

1. _____

2. _____

3. _____

4. _____

5. _____

6. _____

7. _____

8. _____

9. _____

10. _____

11. _____

12. _____

13. _____

14. _____

15. _____

16. _____

17. _____

18. _____

19. _____

20. _____

21. _____

22. _____

23. _____

24. _____

25. _____

26. _____

27. _____

28. _____

29. _____

30. _____

Seeds of inspiration can be found in any moment.

- Helene Pam

30 Day Exercise Challenge

My Goal: _____   Start Date: _____

1 2 3 4 5

6 7 8 9 10

11 12 13 14 15

16 17 18 19 20

21 22 23 24 25

26 27 28 29 30

46

30 Day Exercise Challenge

Track the amount of exercise you do for 30 days.

My Goal: _____ Start Date: _____

1 2 3 4 5

6 7 8 9 10

11 12 13 14 15

16 17 18 19 20

21 22 23 24 25

26 27 28 29 30

30 Day Reading Challenge

My Goal: _____ Start Date: _____

1

2

3

4

5

6

7

8

9

10

11

12

13

14

15

16

17

18

19

20

21

22

23

24

25

26

27

28

29

30

30 Day Reading Challenge

My Goal: _____   Start Date: _____

1

2

3

4

5

6

7

8

9

10

11

12

13

14

15

16

17

18

19

20

21

22

23

24

25

26

27

28

29

30

Acts of Kindness Challenge

My Goal: _____   Start Date: _____

1 2 3 4 5

6 7 8 9 10

11 12 13 14 15

16 17 18 19 20

21 22 23 24 25

26 27 28 29 30

50

Acts of Kindness Challenge

Track how many acts of kindness you do for 30 days.

My Goal: _____ Start Date: _____

1

2

3

4

5

6

7

8

9

10

11

12

13

14

15

16

17

18

19

20

21

22

23

24

25

26

27

28

29

30

30 Days of Doodles

Draw what comes to mind for 30 days.

1	2	3	4	5
6	7	8	9	10
11	12	13	14	15
16	17	18	19	20
21	22	23	24	25
26	27	28	29	30

30 Days of Doodles

Draw what comes to mind for 30 days.

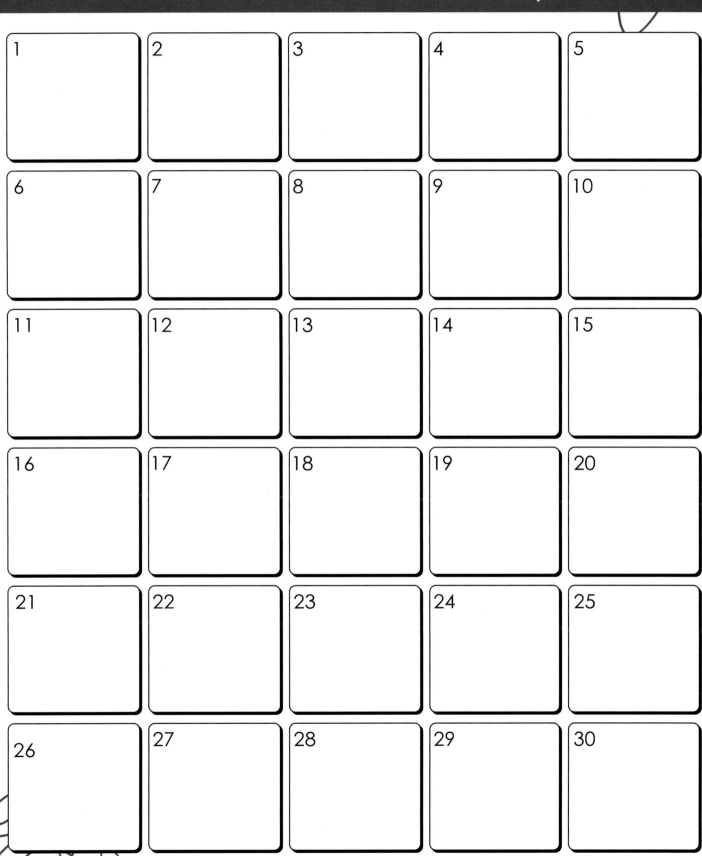

1	2	3	4	5
6	7	8	9	10
11	12	13	14	15
16	17	18	19	20
21	22	23	24	25
26	27	28	29	30

Create your own 30 day challenge.

My Goal: _____ Start Date: _____

Why: _____

1	2	3	4	5
6	7	8	9	10
11	12	13	14	15
16	17	18	19	20
21	22	23	24	25
26	27	28	29	30

54

Create your own 30 day challenge.

My Goal: _____ Start Date: _____

Why: _____

1	2	3	4	5
6	7	8	9	10
11	12	13	14	15
16	17	18	19	20
21	22	23	24	25
26	27	28	29	30

55

Reflection

What have I enjoyed the most the last few months?

What are some valuable things that I have learned?

What are some things that I can still improve?

What do I want to continue doing?

How am I going to celebrate the progress I have made?

You did it!

You have completed your Self-Care Planner. Awesome job!

We hope that you have enjoyed working through your Self-Care
Planner and got a lot of value out of the activities and process.
For additional worksheets and templates, you can find
self-care planner printables on our website.

We would love to stay connected. You can find
Purple Splash Studios on Facebook, Instagram, and Twitter.
Please share your stories, experiences, and photos and
post a review on Amazon to help spread the word.
You can visit our website to discover more self-growth
and meaningful printables and books for all ages.

www.PurpleSplashStudios.com

ISBN 13: 978-1-7328213-0-9

Made in the USA
Monee, IL
15 June 2021